Sheep block the village high street at Market Lavington, Wiltshire, in 1930.
OPPOSITE: *Clipping a sheep, from Stephens's 'The Book of the Farm'.*

SHEPHERDING TOOLS
AND CUSTOMS

Arthur Ingram

Shire Publications Ltd

CONTENTS

Photography by Malcolm Harris.

Printed in Great Britain by City Print (Milton Keynes) Ltd., Simpson Road, Bletchley, Milton Keynes

Two types of yoke for preventing sheep escaping (see page 24).

A Soay ram, a breed closely resembling the first domesticated sheep. Remains of this type of sheep have been discovered in neolithic and bronze-age middens.

INTRODUCTION

Most people think of Britain's wealth as stemming from industry and finance, from coal, steel and manufactured goods. This for the past 150 years has been true. But for many centuries before the industrial revolution, Britain's wealth was built on her trade in wool.

The domestic sheep was certainly established in the bronze age and was probably herded by neolithic man. These early sheep were probably rather goat-like in appearance and were kept as much for their milk as for their fleece. The Romans recognised the potential of Britain for producing wool and they established large-scale sheep farming. England was trading in wool at the time of the Norman invasion, and this trade gradually grew and flourished through medieval times, reaching its peak in the eighteenth and early nineteenth centuries, when the chalk uplands of England were teeming with sheep.

At this time many large landowners saw the potential of the Scottish Highlands as sheep-rearing land and filled the glens and hillsides with their flocks, to the exclusion of the crofting families and their livelihood. So to many people the advance of the sheep did not mean prosperity, but to others they were a whole way of life. The shepherd was such a man. He was also a highly regarded rural artisan, employing methods and implements peculiar to his own calling, most of which have passed with time.

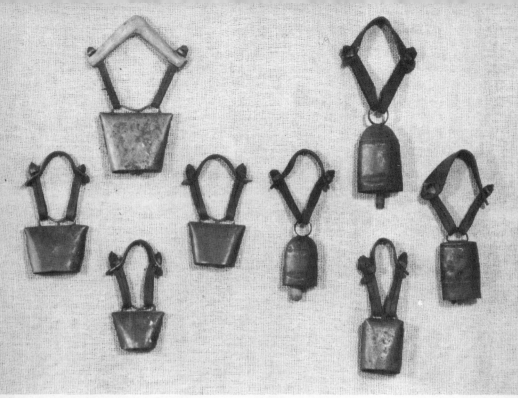

ABOVE: *Sheep bells. The left-hand four are clucket bells, made by William Lancaster, of Great Cheverell, Wiltshire, in the mid nineteenth century. The remaining four are canister bells, three round ones and the lower a squared one.*
BELOW: *Sheep grazing on typical downland sheep country.*

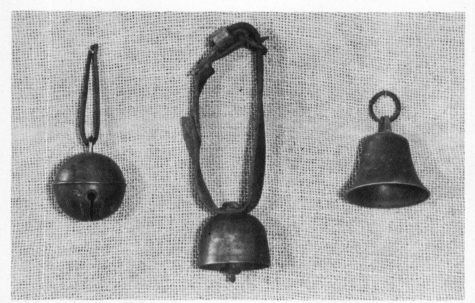

Sheep bells made by bellfounders. Left to right: a crotal or rumbler bell by Robert Wells of Aldbourne, 1760-81; a cup bell by James Burrough of Devizes, 1738-55; and a small latten bell, also by Robert Wells.

SHEEP BELLS

There are two reasons why shepherds might have fitted bells to their sheep when they were herded across downland. The first and most likely reason is that they were fitted as a warning system to aid the shepherd. By listening to the bells the shepherd could tell in what direction and at what distance the sheep were moving. And by the tone of the bells he could tell the state of mind of his flock. When sheep were peacefully grazing the bells emitted a gentle, spasmodic 'chunking' sound; a rhythmic 'clunk-clunk-clunk' meant that they were moving in an orderly manner, probably to fresh grazing or to a nearby dewpond to drink; and an agitated jangling, signifying that the bell was being shaken vigorously, meant the sheep were running, probably in panic, perhaps fleeing a marauding dog. The shepherd could react according to the situation.

The second possible reason is that the shepherd, having great pride in his flock, might fit bells for aesthetic reasons, much as the carter would polish the brasses of his horse harness.

Bells were sometimes fitted to all the sheep in a flock, but this would be expensive for the shepherd, who owned the bells himself though the sheep were his master's. Alternatively they were fitted to dominant ewes, which lesser ewes would follow.

The use of sheep bells was widespread throughout England, particularly in the chalk uplands of the South, ideal sheep country that lent itself to efficient management by an accompanying shepherd. But as one travels north and west their use appears to wane: they were far from abundant in Wales or the Pennines and almost absent from the Highlands of Scotland. The ruggedness of these areas made flock management impracticable, and sheep were enclosed by stone dykes or they roamed in a half-wild state, herded together only for shearing or lambing. In either case bells were unnecessary.

The bells themselves were of various metals and were constructed in a variety of ways. Bells from the eighteenth and nineteenth centuries fall into two main groups: sheet-metal bells, usually made by an animal-bell maker or the local smith; and bells cast in bell-metal by an established bellfounder.

The first group came in various shapes and sizes and manners of construction. Firstly there was the *clucket* or *clucker* bell. Seen face on, its shape is that of a flattened rectangle, tapering towards its mouth. Seen from its side, it tapers towards its top. It was made of a single piece of sheet metal a sixteenth of an inch thick and so fashioned that it folded into shape, being riveted at either side and clasped together at the top. The clapper, an iron stem with a bulbous head, was fixed inside to an iron ring at the top. At the top on the outside was a metal fitting shaped like a flattened 'M'. To this were attached the straps for hanging the bell round the animal's neck. This type was the most easily made and widespread.

Another type of sheet-metal bell, often made alongside the clucket, was the *squared canister*. Like the clucket, it was made of one piece of metal, folded, riveted and clasped into shape, but its shape was akin to that of a corned-beef tin. Its clapper and the lugs for the straps were similar to those of the clucket. The *round canister* was not as widespread as the squared canister, as its construction necessitated brazing. This was an added sophistication, not always appreciated by the simple bell-maker. Its basic construction of sheet metal one sixteenth of an inch thick, curved and riveted to form an open cylinder, was the same, but the top of the bell, either a flat round or a domed round section, had to be brazed to the cylinder. The clapper might be the same as in the squared canister or might be a tongue of wood or bone. The strap-fitting lug was circular and brazed or clipped to the apex.

These bells came in varying sizes, often in sets, from as small as 3 inches across, often up to well over 6 inches. This provided a change of tone, by which the shepherd could recognise individual sheep. Another process by which the tone could be varied was dipping the bell in brass: the thicker the coating of brass, the more resonant was the tone.

The second group of bells, those cast by bellfounders, was less widespread, almost certainly because they were more expensive. Much the most extensively used of these was the *cup bell*, shaped like an upturned cup and cast in bell-metal. The clapper was of similar design to those used in sheet-metal bells. The strap lug was simply a metal stud over which fitted a metal plate with a hole in it; this was kept in place by a pin through a hole in the stud.

The *latten bell* is the bell-shaped bell. It, too, was cast in bell-metal and had a metal clapper, the strap lug being usually similar to that of the cup bell.

The *crotal bell*, often called a *rumbler*, was cast as a complete sphere and had a single opening consisting of two holes connected by a slit. Inside the bell was a metal ball which rolled about as the bell moved, so doing the job of the clapper.

Sheep bells were secured round the animal's neck, usually with leather straps and in conjunction with a *yoke*.

The yoke was either a broader band of leather which rested on the nape of the sheep's neck, or of wood or occasionally of bone. The wooden yoke was shaped like a shallow inverted 'V' and was carved, usually by the shepherd himself. Having chosen a suitably shaped piece of branch wood, often from a gorse bush, he would trim it flat and smooth with his clasp-knife. He would then make oblong holes at either end of the yoke for the leather strap. Then he would carve two shaped pegs to secure the strap as it passed through the holes. This done, the bell and yoke were assembled. The leather strap was passed through the strap lug of the bell and taken double up through the oblong hole in one end of the yoke. An eye was cut in the strap and the wooden peg was inserted on the upper side of the yoke. This was then repeated at the other end.

Over many years of use the yokes are polished smooth by the wool of the sheep and, aided by the natural oils from the fleece, take a beautiful patina most pleasurable to the touch.

An alternative method of fitting a bell to a sheep is to use the strap in the manner of a dog collar, secured with either a buckle or a wooden peg.

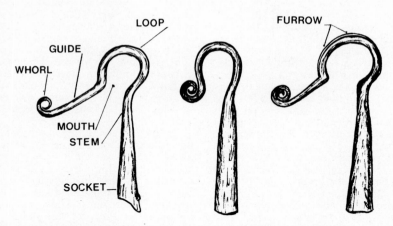

LOOP

FURROW

GUIDE

WHORL

MOUTH

STEM

SOCKET

Shepherds' crooks, from left to right: a leg crook from Marlborough, Wiltshire; a leg crook from north Dorset (notice the absence of a guide); a leg crook with double whorl fashioned from the barrel of an old fowling gun.

SHEPHERDS' CROOKS

It is a popularly believed misconception that the familiarly shaped shepherd's crook had its origins in biblical times, but this is not so, although certainly Victorian and more recent biblical illustrators have portrayed Palestinian shepherds of those times holding crooks. According to the Bible, however, the Palestinian shepherd was equipped with a rod and a staff; the rod was a thick club about 18 inches long, often with a flattened iron spike at one end, and was used to defend sheep and shepherd against predators; the staff was simply a straight, stout wooden pole from 6 to 8 feet in length and used to aid the shepherd when walking or fording streams.

The crook appears to have been an English development from somewhere in the Dark Ages, but its evolution is obscure. Certainly in the seventeenth, eighteenth and nineteenth centuries no shepherd would be without his crook, and it became the hallmark of his trade. At nineteenth-century hiring fairs he would stand amongst the other workers holding his crook as a sign that he was a shepherd in search of employment.

The English crook was normally made of iron, fitted by a socket to a wooden helve, usually of ash or hazel, between 3½ and 5 feet in length. It was usually employed as a *leg crook,* the shepherd using it to secure the sheep by the hind leg, just above the hock. Some English crooks were used to catch the sheep by the neck; these were called *neck crooks* and required a larger iron crook of a differing shape.

A third type of crook used in England was employed only seasonally: this was the *dipping crook* used to immerse the sheep at dipping time. Dipping crooks came in varying designs in both metal and wood and were longer than the leg and neck crooks, being often as much as 9 or 10 feet.

Each shepherd had his own preferences about the design of his crook. He usually took his personal specifications to the local smith, who would skilfully produce the crook he desired.

The leg crook tapered from the socket for about 6 to 8 inches and then curved slightly backwards. It then curved forward in slightly more than half a circle to form the *loop* of the crook. This was normally 1¾ inches across and continued round to the point opposite the slight backward curve where it became the *mouth*. The mouth was approximately 1¼ inches across. The old shepherds tested this for size by passing the broadest part of their thumb through it and were only satisfied if the clearance on either side was narrow. From the mouth the *guide* curved away sharply at an angle of between 45 and 80 degrees and extended for between 2 and 4 inches before terminating in a single, double or occasionally treble *whorl*. It was said that one could tell a shepherd's status by the number of whorls to his crook. A single whorl denoted an under-shepherd, a double whorl a head shepherd. This may only have been a local custom. Some of the most prized crooks were fashioned from the barrel of an old gun; such a crook often had a distinct furrow running along the outside of the loop.

The neck crook was similar in general construction, but larger, the loop being about 4½ inches across and the mouth about the same. It then terminated in a very short guide, or perhaps no guide at all.

Dipping crooks vary greatly in design and construction but almost without exception they had two loops facing in opposing directions, one with its mouth towards the user for lifting the sheep's head clear of the water and another with its mouth facing away from the user to immerse the sheep in the water. Some had more than two loops, but at least two were always opposing. They were made of iron or wood and fitted to a haft from 6 to 10 feet in length.

Wales and the Highlands of Scotland had their own form of wooden neck crooks. The usual manner of construction was to choose a suitably shaped piece of wood, normally hazel or ash; generally a small root bowl about 4 inches in diameter was selected. This should have growing from its base, almost parallel to the main stem, a sucker shoot about 1 inch in diameter and straight for 4 to 5 feet. The root bowl was carved into the crook and the sucker formed the handle. Straight ash or hazel rods were also taken and curved by steaming, in the same manner as walking-sticks, but these were regarded as inferior.

In the Highlands fine specimens were carved from horn. The curved horn of a sheep was taken and the core was removed; it was this core and not the outer sheath of the horn that was used to carve the crook. It was polished and set on an ash or hazel haft. These crooks, or *cromachs* as they are known, are still carved in large numbers, but primarily in an ornate manner for sale to tourists as souvenirs.

The shepherd's reliance on his crook was surpassed only by that upon his dog. And not only in droving the sheep did the crook and the dog combine to aid the shepherd—they could also provide him with his supper. I have heard accounts from old Wiltshire shepherds that, on finding a hare crouched in its form, the shepherd would bid his dog 'bide'. He would then walk in a wide circle, coming up behind the hare, whose gaze was still firmly fixed on the dog sitting some yards in front. The shepherd would then strike the hare a blow on the nape of the neck with his crook.

OPPOSITE: *Shepherds' crooks, from left to right: a nineteenth-century neck crook from the Mendips; two nineteenth-century Wiltshire leg crooks; an early nineteenth-century leg crook from north Dorset; a seventeenth-century Wiltshire leg crook; a nineteenth-century dipping crook from the Mendips; a nineteenth-century dipping crook from Wiltshire.*

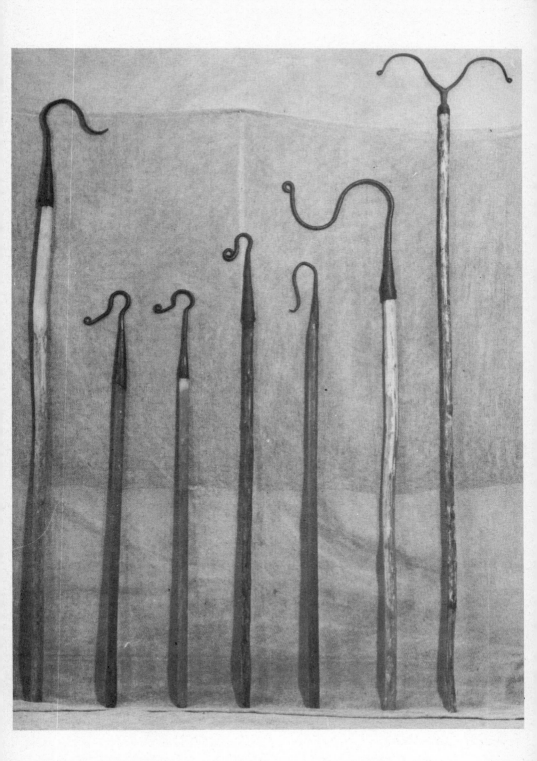

SHEPHERDS' DRESS

Although use of the working smock was widespread amongst other agricultural workers, most people associate it with the shepherd. The wearing of the smock gradually died out from the early nineteenth century and few were worn later than 1870.

The smock was in effect a simple overall. Usually homespun from a durable material such as hemp or flax, it was very generously cut to allow freedom of movement. When the material was cut out in preparation for assembling the smock, each component part—front, back, arms, collar—was rectangular. There are no curved seams in the true smock. Most smocks were revers"'le, being identical front and back; this helped to even out the wear, thus prolonging the life of the garment. Shepherd's smocks usually came to well below the knee. They fitted loosely and had wide square collars. Some had side pockets, some were without, but all were gathered at the chest and cuffs. This was done with a smocking stitch, which varied considerably from smock to smock. Some beautiful examples survive. Most smock sleeves were also gathered at the shoulder with the same ornate but practical stitch. Between the gathering panel on the chest and the sleeve was an area called the *box*, and this and the broad collar were often ornately embroidered with designs depicting the trade of the wearer. Such things as crooks or sheep were often incorporated in the design on a shepherd's smock.

The colour of the smock also varied from locality to locality. White or natural stone colour was probably the most common, but blue, brown, green and occasionally black prevailed in certain areas. The stitching on white or natural smocks was normally white, although in coloured smocks the colour of stitch varied.

Under his smock the shepherd wore his normal linen or woollen shirt and coarse breeches tied just above the ankles with twine or thrust into leather buskins. He was shod with stout leather boots, probably steeped in goose grease or neat's-foot oil to render them water-repellent. Many shepherds also carried a cape made of coarse linen or a material called drabbet which had been treated with oil or pitch to make it water-resistant.

OPPOSITE: *A Wiltshire smock c.1860, with a nineteenth-century leg crook fashioned from an old gun barrel, and an early nineteenth-century wooden costrel.*

HURDLES

Although sheep used to roam and graze over large tracts of land with little restriction to their freedom, there were occasions when they had to be confined, such as at lambing time, or when the shepherd needed to group certain animals together before driving them to the market or sheep fair, or when 'folding' the flock over root crops such as turnips.

The hurdle was in effect a portable, woven, wooden fence that came in sections. It was light, durable and, if erected correctly, stockproof. It was the ideal answer to the shepherd's need for fencing that could be quickly erected or dismantled anywhere he wished.

The construction of hurdles was a craft of the woodland coppice and not of the open sheep country. It grew steadily with the wealth dependent on sheep and the woollen industry and declined with it also.

There were two distinct forms of hurdle, the wattle hurdle and the gate hurdle. Both types were used for the same

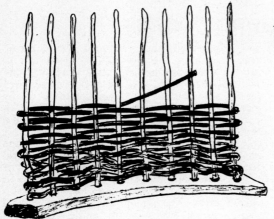

A partially constructed wattle hurdle seated in the curved break. The uprights are called sails.

purpose, often in conjunction with each other. While individual shepherds may have preferred one to the other, both were equally functional.

The *wattle hurdle* was possibly the more widely used. To make it, green hazel rods about ¾ inch in diameter and 8 feet long were cut from the coppice. These were usually cleft in two with a billhook, although they were occasionally used in the round. Other hazel rods were cut, 1 to 1½ inches in diameter and 3½ feet long, and left in the round. The hurdlemaker now had all the materials he needed; no wire, nails or metal of any kind were used in the hurdle, but a strong cunning pair of hands, an appreciation of the characteristics of the materials and a long experience of fashioning them were necessary.

To construct the hurdle the maker first laid on the ground his *break*. This was a beam of wood approximately 4 feet long (for a 4-foot hurdle), 6 inches wide and 4 inches deep, slightly curved in a gentle horizontal crescent. In this were bored ten holes and into these holes were placed vertically ten of the 3½-foot hazel rods. These rods were known as the *sails* and between them the hurdlemaker wove the 8-foot rods. As the end of one was reached another was expertly 'let in'. In order that the end sails would not fall away, the rods were bent round them and woven back in the opposite direction. This process was probably the most skilled and exacting of the craft. For to bend the rods this acutely without snapping them the hurdlemaker had to twist the rod at the same time as

bending it back upon itself, thus twisting the wood fibres to eliminate splintering. This was a most difficult action calling for a strong wrist and a knack acquired from experience. As the hurdle was built up the maker from time to time exacted pressure on it with his knee to compress the rods more tightly. The rods in the top row woven across were often thinner than the rest and woven more precisely, giving a neat and secure finish known as *ethering*. The hurdle was now nearly complete as it stood slightly bowed in its break.

Making the hurdle on a curve was of prime importance for two reasons: firstly it enabled the maker to weave it more tightly, and secondly it allowed for drying out and subsequent shrinkage of the green hazel.

The hurdle was then taken from its break and the rough ends were trimmed with a billhook. It was then stacked to dry out and await a customer.

The *gate hurdle* was perhaps simpler in construction but the materials needed more complex preparation. Ash, oak or chestnut was used. First the hurdlemaker would cleave stakes of the various lengths desired with an implement known as a *fromard*. This was a L-shaped tool, the upright of the 'L' being the wooden helve and the iron head the horizontal stroke. The cutting edge faced downwards and was forced through the wood along the grain by striking the rear edge of the blade with a wooden *bittel,* which rather resembled a one-handled rolling-pin. Other regional names for the fromard

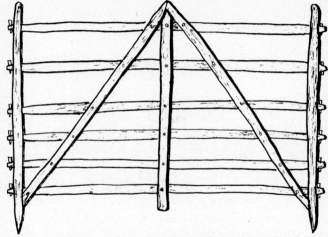

A gate hurdle made of cleft ash, oak or chestnut. The ends of the horizontal members are morticed with wooden pegs.

include reamer, thrower, throw-axe, side-knife, froe, froward, frummer and frammer. The last four names and the term 'fromard' are probably derived from the act of using the tool away from one's body and never towards it. This tool was only used to cleave wood along the grain and never to cut across it.

The staves of the hurdle, having been cleft, were trimmed into shape with a draw-knife or hurdlemaker's hatchet. The mortices were then formed by drilling with a brace and bit or auger into the two uprights. Six holes were drilled in each to take the six crossbars. These bars were tapered so that they fitted into the mortices with about one inch protruding through the upright on the outside of the hurdle. Through these protruding butts

smaller holes were bored and in these cleft wooden pegs were hammered. This drew the hurdle together into a reasonably secure entity. However, to strengthen it still further, one stave was fixed, by nailing or wooden pegs, vertically down the six crossbars, and two more ran across diagonally from the top centre to opposing bottom corners. The end product was light, sturdy and versatile.

In England in the eighteenth and nine-teenth centuries hazel, ash, and oak were coppiced specifically for the hurdling trade and were bought and felled by the hurdlemaker every seven years or so. Most villages in sheep country had at least one hurdlemaker, and very often more. How-ever, the decline of the woollen industry, the ploughing of traditional sheep grazing

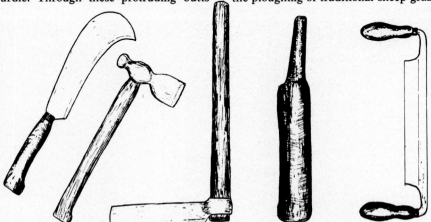

Hurdlemakers' tools, from left to right: spar hook, hatchet (with hammer end for driving in wooden pegs), fromard, bittel, and draw-knife.

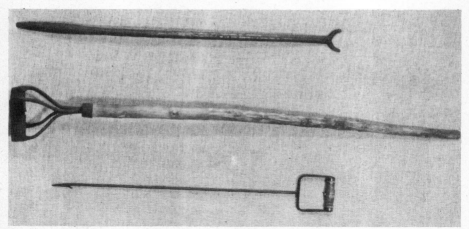

From top to bottom: A shepherd's fold pitcher used in setting up hurdles; a turnip chopper; a wool-bale sampler.

and the resultant reduction in the number of sheep, together with the introduction of new forms of fencing, ensured the gradual demise of the craft, though individual craftsmen can still be found who answer a demand far removed from shepherding—that of the suburban gardener.

The shepherd used hurdles for 'folding' his sheep. Confining sheep in such a manner was necessary for various reasons, one of which was the practice of folding sheep over turnips. This was common winter practice in the eighteenth and nineteenth centuries. A pen of hurdles was set up at the edge of a field of turnips and the sheep were turned into it. As that area of turnips was consumed by the sheep so the hurdle pen was moved on, and so on until the whole patch of turnips had been grazed.

The setting up of hurdles was usually done with an implement called a *fold pitcher*. This was a sturdy iron bar about 3 feet 6 inches long and 2 inches in circumference, widening to a bulbous point some 4 inches in circumference. At the other end it branched into a shallow 'V' to accommodate the shepherd's

A portable sheep-feeding crib, made of cleft ash by the hurdlemaker.

Sheep pennings overlooking the Vale of Pewsey.

thumb. This implement was thrust into the ground forming holes into which the pointed butts of the hurdle were dropped. Hurdles were supported at intervals by posts known as *shores*, to which the hurdles were attached with twine or twisted hazel bonds.

The folding of sheep across turnips ensured the concentrated manuring of the ground they were grazing, so it was a most economical way of winter-feeding sheep. In some areas sheep are still folded across root crops, but today it is termed *strip feeding*, and the hurdles have been replaced by plastic sheep netting and electrified fences.

The folding of sheep was also necessary before driving them to market or the annual sheep fair. Sheep were enclosed in their hurdle compounds, counted, graded and selected. Those considered suitable were driven by the shepherd to market, in some cases many miles away. Hurdles were also used at the market to pen the sheep while awaiting auction.

Another occasion when sheep needed folding was at lambing time when the ewes in lamb were brought into the security of the fold so that they and their offspring would be easily accessible to the shepherd in event of difficulties. Ewes were often folded in individual pens, although on other occasions they were grouped in small hurdled paddocks. If the lambing was taking place early in an exposed area, the hurdles were often thatched with hay or

straw to give extra protection against the biting winds. This was done by sewing the thatch on to the hurdle with twine, using a *hurdle needle*. The hurdle needle was usually cut from a branch of ash or hazel about 2½ inches in circumference and tapered down to a point. An eye was bored at the broad end to receive the twine. The needle was normally about 18 inches long.

Hurdles found other odd uses in the hands of the shepherd: they were used as temporary blocks in a breached hedge or stone dyke. In the days before the advent of the shepherd's hut, he would often thatch a hurdle and placing it on end, he would lean it against two shores to provide a crude shelter against the wind. Hurdles were also used as makeshift biers on which dead sheep were carried from the field, and injured land workers have been stretchered in the same way.

Another article made for the shepherd by the hurdlemaker was the *sheep-feeding crib*. It was made in bowed cleft ash fitted into a rectangular ash frame some 6 feet by 18 inches. The frame was laid horizontally and holes were bored about 8 inches apart down both the long sides. Thin cleft ash bars were fixed down the holes on one side and bowed over to fix the other ends in the corresponding holes on the opposite side. These cribs were used to feed hay to sheep in the field, as they prevented wind from blowing it away. They were most widely used in Gloucestershire, Somerset and Wiltshire.

15

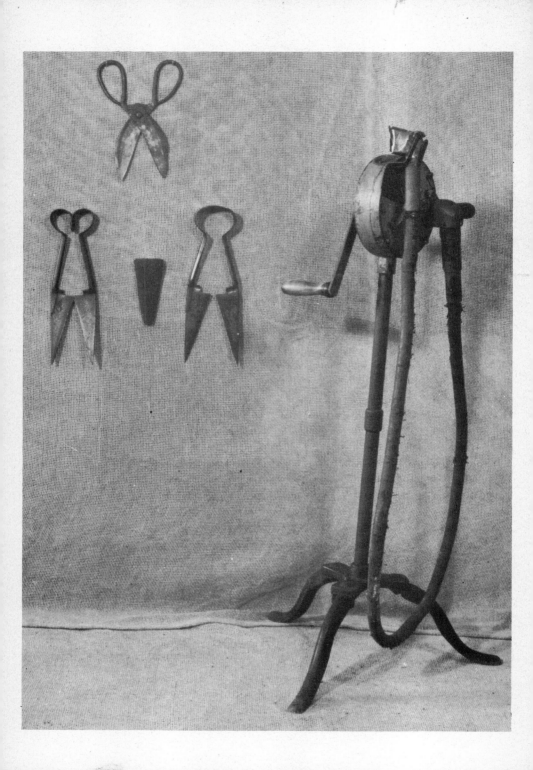

ABOVE: *The Chirton sheep-shearing gang at Meech Farm, Market Lavington, Wiltshire, in 1892.*
OPPOSITE: *Sheep-shearing equipment: top left, eighteenth-century scissor shears; bottom, two pairs of nineteenth-century spring-tined shears with a leather sheath; right, hand-cranked, mechanical sheep clippers, c.1906.*

SHEARING THE SHEEP

The time of year for shearing varied from late May to mid August, according to the part of the country. Shearing was the culmination of the sheep farmer's year. The shepherd himself usually took part in the shearing, but he did not shear the entire flock on his own. Shearing gangs of a dozen men or more were employed. These men were often itinerant for the duration of the shearing season, travelling from flock to flock as their hiring demanded. They were hard-working, often hard-drinking and boisterous fellows, and they could shear sheep in a remarkably short time using hand *shears*, or *dags* as they were often called. Throwing a sheep on its back, the position in which it was most helpless, they would clip the sheep leaving the fleece as entire as possible.

Until the late eighteenth century the shears used took the form of large scissors about 10 inches long. They were normally made by a local blacksmith. These were gradually displaced by the *spring-tined shears*, which had two triangular scissor-shaped blades connected by a loop of spring steel, so that when the blades were brought together by the hand to a cutting position they would spring back apart ready for the next cut. This type of shears remained in use until the adoption of mechanical shearing around 1900.

The earliest *mechanical shearers* worked by a series of cogs and bearings, and connecting rods. A handle terminated in a cog; this fed another cog which in turn rotated a third cog. These were geared to build up the differential between the speed the operator turned the handle and the speed of the drive off the last cog. These cogs were housed in a cylindrical box. Issuing from this box was a flexible steel coiled cable, covered in a thin canvas sheath. This cable was about 6 feet long and was in effect the drive-shaft, for through its hollow core ran a series of metal rods connected loosely by loops. These ran from the last cog to the shearing head and by twisting they caused the teeth of the clipping head to reciprocate. The clipping head was used by the shearer in much the same manner as the modern electric clipper. The whole thing stood on a single tubular leg which terminated in a broad tripod. This description is of trimmers manufactured by the Stewart Company in 1906; at about the same time the Wolseley Company was producing a similar machine, but the differential on this model was achieved by incorporating a large crank wheel 30 inches in diameter connected to a bicycle chain.

The shorn wool was packed into bales for sale to the merchants. The baling of wool gave an opportunity for sharp practice that was eagerly taken by some of the less scrupulous. The bale was often packed so that good-quality fleece surrounded an inner core of inferior matted fleece, and it was not unknown for the centre of a bale to contain no more than hay or rags. It was impracticable for the merchant to untie, search and repack every bale upon purchase, so this ploy often went unnoticed until it was too late, and when eventually discovered it was to the merchant's loss. But merchants were not without their own cunning, and they began to use an implement called a *wool-bale sampler*. It was a simple device —no more than a thin metal shank 30 inches in length, surmounted by a framed wooden cross-piece handle and terminating in a point from which sprang two backward-facing barbs. If thrust into a wool bale and withdrawn this implement would contain on its barbs a sample of the material forming the centre of the bale.

If the farmer had overdone the substitution of materials this might also show up on the weighing of the wool. A device much used for this, after its introduction in the 1850s, was *Manchur's balance*. This was an ingenious weighing device which worked on a principle using the tension of steel. A band of tempered steel an eighth of an inch thick and about half an inch wide was formed in an 'O' shape with the ends overlapping but not joined. At the top was fixed a ring for securing the scales, and at the bottom a hook on which was hung the object to be weighed. The tension on the O-shaped frame caused by this weight pulled it slightly apart. This caused a needle fixed to one terminal point of the frame and slotting through an aperture in the other terminal to climb slowly up a crescent-shaped brass scale fitted in the centre of the frame, which ran from nought to 300 pounds. On the reverse of the same brass plate was a scale running from nought to 30 pounds. This was used in conjunction with a smaller loop and hook fitted near the terminal ends and operating the same iron needle. The principle was that of pulling the ends apart by applying weight against metal tension. The use of this type of scale was declared illegal in 1907 owing to its alleged inaccuracy. Many other types of scales were used to weigh wool but Manchur's remains, if not the most accurate, probably the most ingenious.

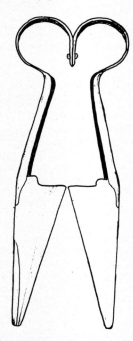

ABOVE: *Spring-tined sheep shears or 'dags', with points rounded to protect the sheep's hide.*
OPPOSITE ABOVE: *A sheep-shearing shed at Chilmark, Wiltshire.*
OPPOSITE BELOW: *A pair of Shetland sheep.*

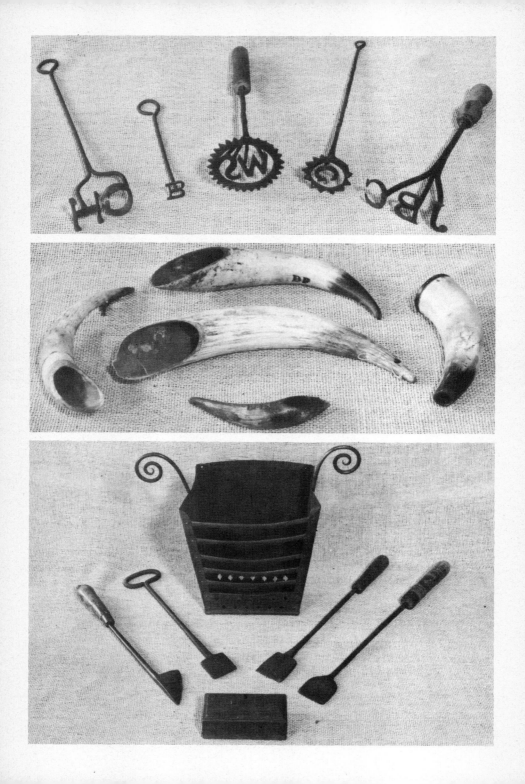

ABOVE: *Clockwise from left: a shepherd's saw for trimming overgrown horns; a salve box for ointment; Manchur's balance for weighing wool; a hurdle needle used to thatch hurdles with straw.*
OPPOSITE: *From top to bottom: sheep-branding irons; drenching horns for administering medicine to sheep; a shepherd's brazier with four docking irons and an iron docking block.*

SHEPHERDS' TOOLS AND AIDS

The shepherd had to be able to identify his sheep in case they were stolen or strayed. The most permanent means of identification was branding. This was done with a *branding iron* before the young sheep commenced their first 'full wool'. These irons had an iron shank terminating in a head fashioned in a manner peculiar to its owner; often his initials or a simple design such as a sun, crescent or star, or often a combination of the two. The iron was heated in red-hot embers and the design was burnt on to the animal's flesh.

Another type of branding iron had a much smaller head and was usually fashioned numerically, each iron being an individual number. These were used to brand the horns of the sheep as a means of

identifying the individual animal within the flock. This method became defunct when horned sheep declined in popularity. Skin branding was replaced at the end of the nineteenth century by the use of pitch, which was often applied hot with the old branding irons, and coloured dyes.

The hot embers needed to heat the branding irons were brought into the field in a *brazier*. Some nineteenth-century blacksmith-made examples were works of fine craftsmanship, with beautifully worked iron handles for carrying.

The *lamb's tail docker* was heated in a similar fashion to the branding iron. This implement had an iron shank, some 6 to 10 inches long, which terminated in a small spade-like head about 2 inches across and 3 inches deep. The tail of the lamb was placed across a block of stone or iron, and the heated docking iron was allowed to sear gently between the vertebrae of the tail. The heat was enough to sever the tail without the need for a thrusting or chopping motion with the iron. The heated docker also acted as a cauterising agent, sealing off the skin cells and preventing infection. This implement was also known as a *searing iron*.

Other methods of amputating lambs' tails were practised, primarily by constricting the blood supply, causing withering and eventual decay. This was usually done by binding the tail with twine, or more recently with rubber bands. Lambs' tails were not docked for aesthetic reasons, but for the practical purpose of preventing their droppings fouling the thick fleece of the tail and so causing fly infestation.

The treatment of sick sheep was the task not as it is today of the veterinary surgeon with his wide range of modern drugs and antibiotics, but of the humble shepherd with only traditional remedies handed down from generation to generation. Some of these were useful, but others were quite ineffectual; all relied more on the dedication and expertise of the shepherd than on their own remedial powers.

On the grounds that prevention is better than cure, the shepherd went to pains to ensure this his sheep remained healthy. Salving was carried out in the eighteenth and nineteenth centuries in an attempt to prevent skin conditions breaking out beneath the thick fleece of the sheep. For this slow, laborious task each sheep had to be caught, then laid and held down on a *salving stool*. This was a rather pear-shaped three-legged stool slatted at its broad end and formed into a seat at the narrow end. On this seat the shepherd sat while holding the squirming sheep on the slatted section. He then parted the fleece and smeared on the salve. This was a mixture whose ingredients varied, but goose grease, butter, tar and fish oil would be amongst them in varying quantities. Salving was generally done during the autumn to help waterproof the fleece and to protect the sheep against scab and parasite infestation. This type of salve was also applied as a remedy for footrot, a complaint all too common in sheep.

Many shepherds used an aid known as a *salve box*. This was a small box about 4 inches long and 3 inches broad, often carved from a solid piece of wood. At the front, also carved from the solid, projected a lip cunningly shaped to take the ball of the thumb. The base of the box was carved to a concave shape which fitted neatly to the user's wrist, to which it was secured by a broad leather strap tied with thongs. When strapped to the wrist, the box was filled with the salve, and the shepherd dipped his thumb into it, smearing off the excess on the thumb-shaped projection. Wearing this simple appliance, the shepherd had a supply of salve ready to hand and still had both hands free to restrain the sheep and treat it.

Salving was slowly replaced in the nineteenth century by the practice of *dipping*. Sheep were guided through a trough of disinfectant water, controlled by the shepherd with his dipping crook. The dipping of sheep was made compulsory by an order introduced in the late nineteenth century. It was carried out in the autumn and spring, with a police constable present to supervise proceedings. Spring dipping was calculated to clean and condition the fleece for shearing.

Administering medicines for internal disorders is today done mainly with injections, but in the eighteenth and nineteenth centuries the shepherd administered medicines orally in draughts called drenches. To aid him in forcing the medicine down the sheep's throat he used a *drenching horn*. This was simply a cow's horn of suitable size, with the core removed and the broad end cut off obliquely to form a lip. Alternatively the narrow end of the horn was cut off, leaving a hole about three quarters of an inch in diameter, and the other end was stopped up with a wooden bung. To administer the drench the animal's jaws were forced apart and the drenching horn was placed to the back of the throat, the contents then being poured down.

When difficulty was experienced in handling the animal, as was often the case with an obstreperous ram, the shepherd might place it in a restraining *yoke*. This

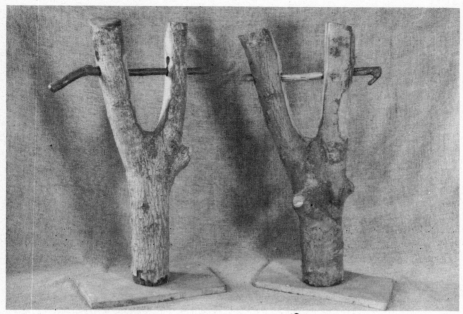

was a very simple device, often no more than a sturdy fork cut from a hedgerow tree and pointed at its base. This was either driven deep into the floor of a shearing shed as a permanent fixture, or was used portably, being driven into the ground as the need arose. The sheep's neck was then dropped into the 'V' of the fork. Sometimes a wooden pin was pushed through two holes towards the top of the fork, passing across the nape of the sheep's neck so that it could not lift its head. Nor could it withdraw its head as its jowls were too wide. Restrained thus, it made the job of administering the draught much less laborious.

An instrument called the *shepherd's mate* was also used similarly. This was a rectangular wooden frame. The verticals were sharpened and tipped with iron, and above the top horizontal they were bound with iron ferrules to prevent splitting when they were struck with a mallet. At one bottom corner another wooden bar was fixed with an iron pin to form a pivot. This bar lay diagonally across the frame. At the point of intersection with the top horizontal a rectangular aperture was cut in it, and the horizontal passed through this. A

TOP: *Sheep-retaining yokes, originally embedded in a shearing-shed floor.*
ABOVE: *A shepherd's mate was another means of restraining sheep for treatment.*

23

An iron sheep collar, fitted to prevent the animal from turning and nibbling wounds, and a yoke to prevent sheep escaping through gaps in hedges (see page 2).

hole was bored in the diagonal so that by moving it on its pivot it might be brought to correspond with one of the three other holes bored in the horizontal. An iron pin was then pushed through to lock the diagonal in place. This implement was portable and was hammered upright into the ground. The sheep's head was held between the locked diagonal and one of the uprights. This was also used for treatments or the occasional difficult shearing.

Another type of yoke was fitted to a sheep that persistently escaped, and there was such an animal in most flocks. Once it had found a method of forcing its way between hurdles or through gaps in hedges, then it would continue to do so with galling regularity, often taking others with it. Two kinds of yoke were used to check this. One consisted simply of a chain or leather strap threaded through a pole about 3 feet long, so that the pole balanced perfectly on either side in a horizontal position. The strap was fitted round the sheep's neck so that the pole hung just in front of the legs. When the animal attempted to force its way through a gap,

the pole became jammed across it. The second type consisted of three batons of wood nailed in a crude triangle around the sheep's neck. This acted in exactly the same manner to prevent its escape.

Another contrivance designed to fit around the sheep's neck was the *sheep collar*. This was an iron cage that had two horseshoe-shaped ends 6 inches apart joined by four narrow iron rods. It fitted on the sheep's neck and was secured by leather thongs, which were fixed to eye holes at the four corners of the frame. It was fitted to a sheep that had a skin wound or condition which the shepherd wished to stop it from licking or nibbling. The collar prevented the animal from turning its head.

Another implement often used by the shepherd was a small *saw*. It was usually no more than 9 inches long with a very narrow blade, similar to a keyhole saw, and a short curved wooden handle. The shepherd could carry it with him as he tended his flock. He used it to cut back inward-growing horns, which might otherwise grow into the eye socket, blinding the animal, or into the flesh of the skull,

Early lanterns: left and right have windows of beaten horn; the centre one has glass.

causing unsightly suppurating wounds. He could quickly saw off the point of a horn that was growing at an unsatisfactory angle. These saws disappeared with the gradual perfecting of hornless varieties of sheep in the nineteenth century.

Obstetrical or lambing forceps were used to assist in manipulating lambs at a difficult birth. They varied in design but were basically an X-shaped metal instrument pivoted in the centre like scissors. The ends of the arms were either slightly curved or spoon-shaped to grip the extremities of the lamb as it lay wrongly positioned in the ewe's uterus. These forceps came on to the market in the 1890s; previously the shepherd had turned the lamb by hand.

Emergencies such as difficult lambings often occurred at night. Light was essential in such circumstances and for centuries it was supplied by the *shepherd's lantern*. There were many different types of lantern but before the mid eighteenth century most had certain widespread characteristics: they were usually made of tin, cylindrical in shape, but sloping at the top to an apex; around this sloping top there were usually three or four vents, with another vent at the apex. To serve as windows the narrow tin strip frames held sheets of beaten horn, as glass was scarce and less durable. A hinged and windowed door opened outward to reveal a simple candle-holder clipped to the base. The horn was translucent and emitted a soft light from the candle within, but this was sufficient for most purposes.

As glass became more plentiful and less expensive in the latter half of the eighteenth century it was used increasingly for the lantern windows and gradually replaced horn. It had the advantage of being transparent, therefore not diffusing the already weak light of the candle. Glass-windowed lanterns remained very similar in design to horn-windowed ones, but the change of material necessitated one alteration. Beaten horn was pliable when steamed and could be curved to follow the contours of the lantern's cylindrical shape. Curved glass was not available to lantern-makers, so they had to contrive a way of incorporating flat sheets of glass into a curved surface. This they did in earlier examples by not having

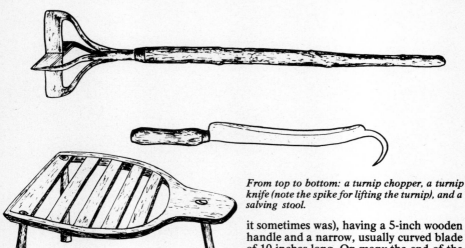

windowing the whole way round, but settling for three or four windows projecting out from the main body of the lantern, rather in the manner of a dormer window. Later the cylindrical shape was often abandoned in favour of a rectangle, and by the mid nineteenth century curved glass had become more accessible and so the variety of designs became manifold.

In the eighteenth and nineteenth centuries the turnip was the winter mainstay of sheep. When sheep were folded across turnips they grazed only the green tops and the upper parts of the roots. The shepherd would go over the ground after the sheep had finished and remove the lower part of the root, still embedded in the ground, with an implement called the *turnip hack*. The head was fitted on a 4-foot wooden helve and had two down-turned iron grains about 6 inches long and 1½ to 2 inches apart. It was used like a hoe on a stubborn weed to grub the turnip root from the ground.

Not all turnips were grazed by sheep; many were grubbed from the ground with the turnip hack and their leaves and taproots were chopped off with a *root knife* or *turnip knife*. This implement looked rather like a sawn-off reaping hook (which

it sometimes was), having a 5-inch wooden handle and a narrow, usually curved blade of 10 inches long. On many the end of the blade tapered to a spike which was curved either backwards or forwards. This very small modification must have been a great boon to the turnip picker, for it meant that by impaling the turnip on the spike he could pick it up with relatively little bending. Often the turnip hack might be dispensed with entirely, if soil conditions permitted, and the turnip was actually grubbed from the ground with the turnip-knife spike.

Having been topped and tailed, as the chopping off of leaves and roots was described, the turnips were taken away and chopped into small fragments for use as sheep fodder. This was done with a *turnip chopper*. The head of this implement consisted usually of four vertical blades about 6 inches long and arranged in an 'X' formation fitted to a 42-inch handle. The user would pound this implement up and down on the turnips until they had been reduced to fragments of the size desired. These were then taken to the sheep in a *fodder scuppit*. This was a wooden trough about 30 inches long, 15 inches wide and 9 inches deep, open at one end. Towards this end the sides tapered slightly. There was a small iron handle at the closed end and a large looped metal handle near the mouth of the scuppit. It was also fitted with four short legs about 3 inches in length. The fodder was scooped up and carried to the sheep in the scuppit.

Shepherd Wilfred Kyte, who taught himself to play the cornet in his solitary existence on Salisbury Plain, seen with his flock and two dogs in the late 1930s.

SHEPHERD DOGS

The shepherd's one constant companion and helpmate was his dog. No single breed could be called the true British sheepdog. The Welsh and Border collies were much used in North and Mid Wales and England. Also widely employed was the small shaggy-haired Bearded Collie. The larger Rough and Smooth Collies were the popular breed in Scotland. Most good shepherds insisted on these dogs of long-proved working strains, although some, less choosey, would settle for a crossbred dog with perhaps retriever or terrier blood. British sheepdogs are all light, nimble, and fleet of foot, bred purely for herding. Their European counterparts such as the Alsatian, the Pyrenean Mountain Dog and the Komondor of Hungary are far larger, more powerful and pedestrian. This is because large predators were exterminated at an early date in Britain allowing the shepherd to concentrate on evolving a specialised herding dog. Wolves and other large predators were prevalent in areas of Europe as late as the nineteenth century, so the continental herdsman was forced to compromise between a herding dog and a guardian for his flock. The Old English Sheepdog might be included in the latter category, but there is no evidence that it was widely used as a true sheepdog in its present form. It was probably derived from Bearded Collie stock and used mainly in a more domestic role.

Training did not begin until the dog was six months old. Every shepherd had his own method of training, but in most cases the pup was first tethered out to watch its parent work sheep and note its reaction to given commands. The next stage was to run the pup with the parent so that it could imitate its manoeuvres. If it showed idleness or a lack of concentration some shepherds would tether the pup to its parent's collar so that it was forced to follow, but this was not always advisable as a slow-learning pup could soon be 'broken' by this method and be of no further use.

Sheepdogs were required not only to herd the sheep but also to separate individuals from the flock, to patrol the flock to ensure it did not overstray its *liberty* (the area of downland on which a shepherd was entitled to graze his flock) and to confine it in a small area to graze a crop of turnips or rape.

A close ally of the sheepdog was the *road dog* used by the drovers to herd sheep over long distances. The road dog was concerned solely with patrolling the flanks of the flock to ensure it did not stray from the ancient drove roads.

The dog's training would normally terminate when it was about one year old, as shepherds considered it then to have lost its receptiveness for learning. This was why a good shepherd was reluctant to use a dog he had not trained himself. For such a dog would have become conditioned to another's idiosyncrasies and find difficulty in adapting to a new master's demands. However, this is not to say that these dogs were not adaptable and quick-witted under one master, for they were often expected to perform complete contradictions. One of the very basics of their training was that they should not give chase to game, but it was considered a very

mediocre dog that did not snatch an illicit rabbit or pheasant when instructed to do so.

Dogs were also required to display the right approach to the sheep. Some were too keen and boisterous, and this trait could prove costly at lambing time. On the other hand, sheep would quickly sense a timid or 'green' dog, turn on it and chase it off. Familiarity with even a good dog would, after a while, often instil contempt for it in the sheep, and they would refuse to react to its herding. The shepherd's answer to this was to borrow a neighbour's dog. This stranger would soon put the sheep back on their toes. After about a fortnight the borrowed dog was returned. The sheep, so reconditioned, then continued to react satisfactorily to the shepherd's own dog.

Sheepdogs worked upwards of fourteen hours a day on a diet of barley meal, often supplied to the shepherd by the landowner as part of his wage. This meagre diet was occasionally augmented by a rabbit paunch or, at lambing time, a ewe's placenta. They led long and active lives and like their masters accepted retirement with quiet loathing. Left behind at farm or cottage in old age, they pined quickly away or passed their last days herding and reherding poultry or even groups of small children to alleviate an acute boredom.

ABOVE: *Wooden costrels and horn cups.* OPPOSITE: *A sheepdog penning sheep.*

THE SHEPHERD AND HIS SHEEP

Into the field along with his crook the shepherd carried his 'bever'—his food and drink for the day. His food, probably bread, cheese and a raw onion, was wrapped in a cloth and carried in a woven rush basket known as a *flail basket*. The drink, usually cider or ale, was carried in a small wooden keg known as a *costrel* or *firkin*. It was either drunk straight from this or from a small horn cup.

In the nineteenth century the *shepherd's hut* provided new comfort for the shepherd. It was a wooden or, later, corrugated-iron shed about 10 feet long, 5 feet wide and 6 feet high and was mounted on four wheels, so it could be drawn by a horse to wherever the flock was grazing. The hut provided shelter from the elements on the exposed downland; it contained a cast-iron stove for heating and cooking and was also normally fitted with a bunk bed. At lambing time the hut was not only the shepherd's daytime shelter, but his home for some weeks.

The hours of the shepherd were long, his responsibilities demanding. But to the farmer, a good and dedicated shepherd was invaluable, and he considered him senior to his other workers. The shepherd's wages (about seven shillings a week in the early nineteenth century) were the highest amongst agricultural workers, at a time when agriculture was by far the largest employer of manpower. Most shepherds were honest dedicated men, who genuinely loved their work and were loyal to their employers. A good shepherd was given an almost free hand by his employer and came to view the flock much as his own property. The shepherd decided when new blood needed introducing to the flock to improve the strain, or when other stock should be sold on, although he could not act on this without consulting with his master.

The sheep were normally sold at the annual sheep fair. Sheep fairs were great social events. While the selling of sheep was their primary purpose, there was usually much more to them than that.

Country folk came from miles around; many of them, particularly the children, had no interest in the price the sheep were making. They had come for the colour of the occasion: the sideshows and stalls of the fair, the local sports including obstacle races and the tug-of-war. Gypsies brought ponies for private barter, and an enormous quantity of ale was consumed. Spending the year isolated on the downs or in his village, the shepherd was glad of the annual opportunity to renew old acquaintances. Often relatives who had moved away to a post some miles distant would only be seen at these events. They would meet, exchange news and views, very often barter for a sheep collie and then go their separate ways for another year.

The manner of counting sheep used by the shepherd in many areas is interesting. Instead of counting 'one, two, three', their counting proceeded as follows: *ain* (1), *tain* (2), *tethera* (3), *methera* (4), *mimp* (5), *ayta* (6), *slayta* (7), *laura* (8), *dora* (9), *dik* (10), *ain-a-dik* (11), *tain-a-dik* (12), *tethera-dik* (13), *methera-dik* (14), *mit* (15), *ain-a-mit* (16), *tain-a-mit* (17), *tethera-mit* (18), *gethera-mit* (19), *ghet* (20). *Gort* was thirty. I obtained this information from Mrs Kathleen Wiltshire of All Cannings in Wiltshire, whose family have had a long history of association with sheep. She could not recall any of the counting beyond thirty-nine, but probably when thirty-nine was reached a notch was cut in a tally-stick and the cycle repeated.

This manner of counting sheep was commoner in northern England and is probably of Nordic origin. Although some of the words may seem longer, when said quickly in sequence they roll off the tongue more fluently. Cornwall, Wales and the Scottish Border Country had similar methods of counting, seemingly peculiar to sheep.

The Cornish method was as follows: *on* (1), *dow* (2), *tray* (3), *pajy* (4), *pemp* (5), *wayth* (6), *sayth* (7), *ayth* (8), *now* (9), *daye* (10), *ignak* (11), *dowthak* (12), *traythak* (13), *peswarthak* (14), *pienthak* (15), *way-thak* (16), *saythak* (17), *sythak* (18), *nowjak* (19), *uggans* (20).

The Welsh method was: *un* (1), *dua* (2), *tri* (3), *pedwar* (4), *pum* (5), *chwe* (6), *saith*

(7), *wyth* (8), *naw* (9), *dig* (10), *warddy* (11), *dueddy* (12), *triarddy* (13), *peswarddy* (14), *peinthaddy* (15), *waythaddy* (16), *saythaddy* (17), *sythaddy* (18), *nowjaddy* (19), *ugain* (20).

Scottish Border Country counting is as follows: *yan* (1), *tyan* (2), *tethera* (3), *methera* (4), *pimp* (5), *sethera* (6), *lethera* (7), *hovera* (8), *dovera* (9), *dik* (10), *yanadik* (11), *tyanadik* (12), *tethera-dik* (13), *methera-dik* (14), *bumfitt* (15), *yana-bumfitt* (16), *tyana-bumfitt* (17), *tethera-bumfitt* (18), *methera-bumfitt* (19), *giggot* (20).

This type of counting has now all but disappeared, as have many of the breeds of sheep formerly counted by it: Norfolk Horn, Wiltshire Horn, Shropshire, Berkshire Knot—evocative names of breeds now extinct or almost so. Many were long, slender, almost goat-like sheep that normally yielded mediocre crops of wool but an excellent quality of mutton. Gradually selective breeding and hybridisation created more economical strains. Smaller sheep, stockier in build and with a thicker fleece, became the goal of stockbreeders in the eighteenth and nineteenth centuries and slowly these were developed. Many of the old breeds bear the name 'horn'. Both sexes of these breeds bore horns, and this was seen as a disadvantage, so breeders tried to eliminate horns, at least in the ewes. Southdown sheep were an early development of this policy: small, stocky, with a dense fleece of high quality, and hornless. They were recognised as a breed in the late eighteenth century. A few Dorset Horns may still be found on their native soil, but the Wiltshire Horn is extinct in its native county, where it once flourished on Salisbury Plain and the high downland. Ironically, the few that do remain are found in Northamptonshire.

The manner in which old breeds were rapidly replaced by more fashionable strains is sharply illustrated by a story concerning the Wiltshire Horn. This breed developed over hundreds of years and had a monopoly within Wiltshire, but it declined swiftly in the eighteenth and nineteenth centuries. At the end of the nineteenth century on the downs near Salisbury an old well was discovered and

A shepherd's hut and (below) a view of the interior, showing the wooden bunk at the rear, a bench and a table. The small cast-iron stove is not visible; it would be to the left of the doorway from which the photograph was taken.

reopened; its bottom was littered with the bones of many scores of sheep. Every skull was horned. This puzzled the farmer, his workers and his friends. Who in his right mind would keep so many rams in his flock, and why did he choose to throw only rams' and not ewes' carcasses down this well? Eventually he was informed that in the old Wiltshire sheep both sexes were horned. The bones in the well were probably the result of the decision of an eighteenth-century sheep farmer to slaughter his flock of 'old-fashioned sheep' and commence his new strain with a clean sheet—a seemingly wasteful exercise, but he could probably find no other market for them if other farmers were of a like mind. It is remarkable that a community as steeped in sheep-rearing tradition as these downlands should lose so totally any recollection of the sheep that were so abundant only a hundred years before.

The shepherd's life was healthy and often a long one. It brought him into close contact with nature and many shepherds became very knowledgeable on the flora and fauna of their district. With time to ponder and evaluate the things they had seen, they often seemed sage-like characters to other rural folk. A good shepherd was almost invariably a much-respected member of the community. He often tended his flock until a very old age and conceding reluctantly to a life of inactive retirement would very often pass on quite shortly afterwards.

A shepherd was often carried to his final resting place on a hurdle bier, and it was a frequently observed tradition to place in his hand a tuft of sheep's wool. This, it was thought, would, upon his arrival at the gates of heaven explain to Saint Peter the reason for his frequent absence from church. Saint Peter, seeing the wool, would realise that he was a shepherd and that ewes lamb on the sabbath also.

Wiltshire Horn sheep, now reintroduced to their native county.